The Invisible Man

H. G. Wells

8575
F
BIN

ILLUSTRATED

Pendulum Press, Inc.

West Haven, Connecticut

ISBN 0-88301-093-3 *Complete Set*
0-88301-131-X *This Volume*

Published by
Pendulum Press, Inc.
An Academic Industries, Inc. Company
The Academic Building
Saw Mill Road
West Haven, Connecticut 06516

Printed in the United States of America

to the teacher

Pendulum Press is proud to offer the NOW AGE ILLUSTRATED Series to schools throughout the country. This completely new series has been prepared by the finest artists and illustrators from around the world. The script adaptations have been prepared by professional writers and revised by qualified reading consultants.

Implicit in the development of the Series are several assumptions. Within the limits of propriety, anything a child reads and/or wants to read is *per se* an educational tool. Educators have long recognized this and have clamored for materials that incorporate this premise. The sustained popularity of the illustrated format, for example, has been documented, but it has not been fully utilized for educational purposes. Out of this realization, the NOW AGE ILLUSTRATED Series evolved.

In the actual reading process, the illustrated panel encourages and supports the student's desire to read printed words. The combination of words and picture helps the student to a greater understanding of the subject; and understanding, that comes from reading, creates the desire for more reading.

The final assumption is that reading as an end in itself is self-defeating. Children are motivated to read material that satisfies their quest for knowledge and understanding of their world. In this Series, they are exposed to some of the greatest stories, authors, and characters in the English language. The Series will stimulate their desire to read the original edition when their reading skills are sufficiently developed. More importantly, reading books in the NOW AGE ILLUS-TRATED Series will help students establish a mental "pegboard" of information — images, names, and concepts — to which they are exposed. Let's assume, for example, that a child sees a television commercial which features Huck Finn in some way. If he has read the NOW AGE Huck Finn, the TV reference has meaning for him which gives the child a surge of satisfaction and accomplishment.

After using the NOW AGE ILLUSTRATED editions, we know that you will share our enthusiasm about the Series and its concept.

—The Editors

about the author

H.G. Wells, an English novelist, sociologist, and historian, was born at Bromley, Kent, in 1866. Through grants and scholarships, Wells attended the Royal College of Science at South Kensington. He graduated in 1888 with honors and went on to earn a B.S. degree from London University. He taught science until 1893 when he turned to journalism.

At the age of twenty-nine, Wells published his first book. He often disguised scientific speculation in the form of fiction as he did in *The Invisible Man,* a scientific romance. In *The War of the Worlds* Wells asks not only what might be, but what ought to be. He exercised an unquestionable influence on his generation as well as later ones.

H.G. WELLS
THE INVISIBLE MAN

Adapted by
OTTO BINDER

Illustrated by
ALEX NINO

a
VINCENT FAGO
production

Mr. Teddy
Henfrey

Mr. Hall

The Invisible Man

Mrs. Hall

Officer Jaffers

Would an Invisible Man rule the world? Could he steal great wealth as an unseen thief? Kill people who stood in his way? Scare the country-side and make people all obey him? That's what the young scientist, Griffin thought—until he found that being invisible caused great troubles and kept him from his evil wishes. His terrible actions only made the whole world his enemy, until he was hunted down like a mad dog.

One cold day in February, a stranger walked into the Coach and Horses Inn, in Iping Village. . . .

A room. . . and a fire! Please! I'm frozen!

Right away, sir.

After the landlady lit a fire in his room, she was surprised when. . . .

Shall I take your coat and dry it, sir?

No, Mrs. Hall. I want to keep it on for now.

As you like, sir. The room will be warm soon.

Later, when Mrs. Hall brought a tray. . . .

Your food, sir.

Oh! You surprised me.

He did not begin to eat, but held his napkin in front of his mouth as he spoke.

You may take those things to dry, Mrs. Hall.

Rather a strange man, he is. . . .

Later. . . .

Sir! Would you mind if Mr. Teddy Henfrey fixes the clock in your room?

You came in again without knocking. . . .

Heavens! Below his nose it looks like his mouth and chin are missing! Or is it my eyes?

Mrs. Hall, I should explain that I am a scientist, and I cannot have people coming in and bothering me while I work. Understand?

Yes, sir! Sorry, sir! Teddy won't take long.

Alone with the strange guest, the repairman was uneasy. . . .

That wrapped-up man gets on my nerves!

You! Get your repairs done fast and get out.

Mr. Henfrey decided to stay longer, but. . . .

It's a simple repair, and you're taking too long.

All right, I'm leaving!

Next day, as the boxes were brought. . . .

Come along with those boxes. I've been waiting long enough.

When the angry guest went outside to talk to the boss. . . .

Listen, mister. . .Oh! Your dog bit me! My leg. . .my hand!

Stop that, you beast!

To everyone's surprise. . . .

My pants leg is torn open! And my glove! Must reach my room quickly!

Sure ran off in a hurry!

The landlady brought her husband to the door. . . .

The dog bit him. He might need a doctor, poor fellow.

I'll go in and see.

In the dark room without a lamp burning. . . .

Sir, are you bleeding? . . .heavens! Your coat sleeve—it has no hand at the end!

You fools!

Get out! I'm not hurt. Just have the rest of my bags brought in. Do you hear?

He's a wild man!

Alone. . . .

There! New pants and a glove, and every inch of my body is covered again. Darn that dog! He nearly gave away my secret.

When the last box had been brought in. . . .

He unpacked more bottles and jars than the drugstore has! And dumped all the straw on the floor. I guess I'll have to clean up.

About this mess. . . .

If it's extra work, put it on my bill. Only get done and get out!

But Mrs. Hall saw something extraordinary. . . .

What! His eyes looked like two big black holes . . .almost as if nothing is there!

In the following days, the sound of bottles smashing and books being thrown about often came from the stranger's room. . . .

What a bad temper he has!

I can't go on! It may take me all my life to finish my work! Darn it all!

Later, bringing tea and cleaning up. . . .

Clean up that broken glass, Mrs. Hall. And never mind talking about extra work! Just put it on my bill!

What can it be that makes him so angry all the time?

He lost his temper every day, as Mrs. Hall could not help hearing.

But sometimes at night, he walked around the town. . . .

Confound it! I have failed again!

He's always talking to himself as if he has a terrible problem. And he seldom leaves his room.

That's the mystery man from the Coach and Horses. He nearly ran us down as if he didn't see us at all!

Oh, mamma! It's the Bogey Man*!

He certainly looks like it.

Meanwhile, throughout town, people had different ideas about the bandaged mystery man.

Bet he's a crook hiding out from the police!

A murderer, that's what!

Naw! Just a harmless nut!

I say he practices black magic.

* an evil spirit, like a ghost

Young people, less frightened, made fun of the stranger.

One day Dr. Cuss, the town's doctor, decided to visit the mysterious stranger. . . .

The doctor met the same shocking surprise Mr. Hall had.

The following Monday night, at the vicarage*, the Reverend Bunting and his wife were suddenly awakened. . . .

Listen! Someone just sneezed downstairs! Go see who it is!

More noises in the library room!

Surrender, you in there. . .what? Nobody here?

Where could that thief hide so quickly? Maybe we only imagined the noises.

Who lit that other candle then? And our money is stolen.

Early in the morning, at the Coach and Horses. . . .

That strange man's clothes are here. . .tossed aside. Where did he go without clothes? When will he come back?

*   the home of the minister

Right now!

Eek! Th-the bed covers are flying away!

Even worse. . . .

That chair. . .it turned upside down and is leaping toward me! It's magic! help!

As the frightened pair fled. . . .

Everything in that room is jumping about. It's ghosts! Eeeaaa!

They even wondered more later when. . . .

Hello, there!

The stranger is back in his room! It-it's impossible!

Recovering from all these strange things, the landlady faced her guest, in the bar.

I don't care what strange things you do. You haven't paid this bill. You said you were expecting money.

I did, didn't I?

The guest took out his stolen money. . . .

Here it is!

All right. But my nerves are going bad, and I have some questions to ask you, if you don't mind.

I want to know how you got in if your room was empty before? And why the chair lifted itself and came at me? And all the other strange things that have been going on. Answer me, sir!

Stamping his foot in great anger, the mystery man yelled back, and . . . .

You dummies! You don't understand who or what I am. I'll show you, by heaven!

Since she was so afraid, Mrs. Hall called the police.

Do your duty, Officer Jaffers! He is a monster.

I don't see his head! Just bread and cheese!

Bravely, the policeman grabbed the headless man. . . .

Got you by the throat, mister!

Let go!

The Invisible Man fought, but the policeman was helped by other men. . . .

Stop! I give up.

That's wise, mister. I'll put the handcuffs on you now.

But the Invisible Man's gloves came off during the fight, and. . . .

Blimey! How can I handcuff a man without hands?

But they might as well have tried to stop a ghost.

And like a tornado, the unseen man rushed through the town uncaught.

Later, the invisible man returned to the inn.

The landlord and landlady caused me trouble all the time. I'll break every window in the place.

But later, he was sorry for the things he had done in the last hour. . . .

I was a fool! My secret is out! Everybody will be looking for me. People will be on guard against me. What am I to do now?

Meanwhile, where Thomas Marvel, the hobo, sat on a bench in another small town nearby. . . .

Looky here! It tells all about an Invisible Man! What a wild story. Do you believe it?

Uh. . .no! It's a big joke.

The truth is, the Invisible Man is here right now, slipping stolen money into my pocket.

Hsst! Keep it safe for me, Marvel.

All through town, a series of silent robberies took place.

Mommy, look! Money floating in the air!

Oh, stop your lies, Tommy. Money doesn't fly around by itself.

But meanwhile a sneaky idea came to the little hobo. . . .

Before the Invisible Man returns for the tenth time, I'll slip away. All the money will be mine! And his notebooks too.

Some time later, a fleeing figure was seen. . .and heard. . .running toward another village.

My word! That man sounds as if his pockets are loaded with coins.

Somehow the Invisible Man trailed me. I hear his breath behind me!

The frightened hobo ran into a bar. . . .

He's coming after me! The Invisible Man! For God's sake, help me! He said he'd kill me. . .and he will! Lock the door!

Open up! Open up, I say.

That's him! Don't let him in! I'll hide here behind the bar.

The next moment. . . .

*As Marvel was dragged away,
one bar customer pulled a gun,
and took bad aim.*

When they tried to grab the unseen man. . . .

In the backyard, the man with the gun fired again.

I'll fire the rest of the shots around the yard, so I'll be sure to hit him.

Yet, when they looked around. . . .

We can't feel any dead body.

I must have missed him, darn it!

That night, at the home of Dr. Kemp. . . .

I heard the doorbell ring.

But there is no one here, sir. Must have been some boy playing tricks.

Wait! Is this blood on the carpet? But how. . .?

Puzzled, he went to his bedroom . . .for another surprise.

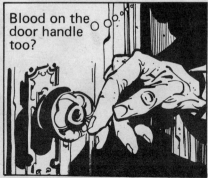

Blood on the door handle too?

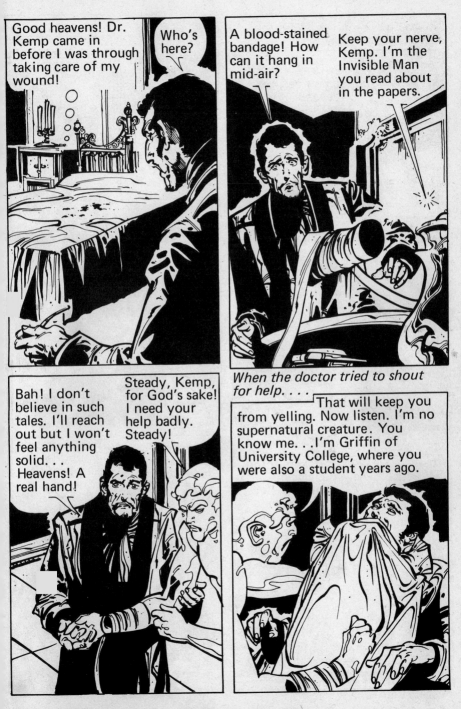

My helper, Marvel, turned me in and tried to make off with money I gave him. When I chased him to a bar, a man shot at me. But forget that. I'll have a cigar now.

It was a strange sight to Dr. Kemp....

Nothing like a good smoke after eating.

How odd! I can see the smoke going into your mouth and throat and down into your lungs as you inhale.

But the money you gave the hobo...where did you get it?

None of your business, Kemp! Right now I'm very tired. I haven't slept for three days and nights.

Help yourself to my bed. Why haven't you slept before?

Because I'm afraid that if I go to sleep, somebody might find me, and I'd be caught.

Oh, what a fool I am! Hope I haven't put that idea into your head, Kemp!

Uh. . .I give you my word I won't turn you in.

Then I can sleep soundly. Good night, Kemp.

He locked the door. He's taking no chances.

Dr. Kemp stayed up, reading the newspaper stories about his strange guest.

The doctor stayed up till dawn, trying to decide what to do.

Good heavens! The man is insane. He's a crazy killer.

TERROR STORY FROM IPING!

WHOLE TOWN IN SUSSEX PANICS!

INVISIBLE MAN STRIKES!

He may do even more horrible things. And he's in my house. What should I do about him? Should I keep my promise not to tell anyone?

No! A promise to a crazy man means nothing. I'll write to Colonel Adye of the Port Burdock police, and tell him to come and capture this invisible man!

A crash sounded upstairs and after the door was unlocked. . . .

What happened, Griffin?

My sore arm pained me as I washed. Had a fit of temper and smashed the bowl. It's nothing.

After Kemp led his unseen guest to the breakfast room.

I want you to be my partner, Kemp. We can do big things together. An invisible man is a man of power!

Before I can promise anything, I must know all about this invisibility of yours.

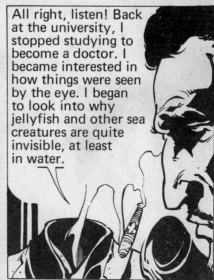

All right, listen! Back at the university, I stopped studying to become a doctor. I became interested in how things were seen by the eye. I began to look into why jellyfish and other sea creatures are quite invisible, at least in water.

The question was, could things be made invisible in air, not water? My studies showed me that besides the coloring of skin and hair and the redness of blood, a man's body cells could easily be made transparent.

And then you found out how to turn even skin, hair, and blood colorless?

Exactly! A chemical mixture could do it, along with the rays from two small dynamos* run by a gas engine. I first tested out my plan on a cat and. . . .

. . . .after it drank the drug, the dynamo rays turned it as invisible as thin air!

It worked! Now I can try it on myself and become the Invisible Man!

* machines that make energy

It worked slowly. First my skin turned pure white. . .
then my whole body became milky, like cloudy
glass. . .then my body began disappearing except
for hair, fingernails, and bones.

"Finally, as the dynamo rays kept working on my body. . . ."

No picture in my mirror! Nothing! The Invisible Man is born!

But the landlord and his two husky step-sons suddenly came in, because of the noise of my dynamos. . . ."

What's going on in here? Make him tell. . .huh?

Nobody here!

"When they went out, wondering, I slipped out with my three notebooks containing the invisibility formulas and. . . ."

I'll mail them to myself at General Delivery at the Great Portland Street Station. I can pick them up later.

"Then I sneaked back into my room and piled up scraps of paper. . . ."

The rest of my chemicals and apparatus I can burn up.

"Of course the whole house burned down. . .but I had to do it, Kemp, to protect my secret!"

"At first, I felt happy when I walked away. . . ."

"But I didn't think about what would happen if others could not see me!"

"Worst of all, two boys with sharp eyes noticed something peculiar. . . ."

Looky! Muddy footprints made by bare feet! Let's follow them.

"Those brats made me run into a yard and painfully climb over a wall."

Who is making these bare footprints? After him!

Those boys told others, and a whole bunch of people are after me, including policemen! How can I escape?

"I stopped and. . . ."

The sun dried the street ahead. If I wipe off this mud, my tracks won't show anymore.

"Though not being chased anymore, I had plenty of small troubles."

My feet are sore. . .my back aches. . .I've got sores where people bumped me . . .and I'm getting a bad cold! Well, at least I'm safe from being followed again.

"I left behind some very puzzled people!"

The footprints ended suddenly, right here! Where did he go? And why was he walking around barefoot, in winter?

Must be out of his head!

"But then, to my horror. . . ."

Of all the bad luck! It's snowing! Now no matter where I run, they can follow me easily. What shall I do?

"An idea flashed into my mind."

I'll slip into this big department store.

Ah, there's what I want. The department selling things for the bedroom.

"And soon, I was happy and warm on a pile of matresses."

Up here, nobody can see the marks my body makes. Now for a nap. I'm dead tired.

"When closing time came, I woke up and. . . ."

When the cleaning people are done, I'll wander around and find what I want.

. . .and I'm all dressed up!

"At last. . . ."

The place is all locked up and I'm alone. Now to visit a half-dozen different departments. . . .

But I may as well sleep the rest of the night. I'll keep my clothes on for an early start tomorrow, leaving the store.

"But I overslept and suddenly sat up to find the store full of clerks ! "

That man! He has no face!

That does it! Now everybody will chase me.

* sales people

I'll hide behind this counter until they give up looking for me.

"Oddly enough, I did not think to take off my clothes and easily escape as the Invisible Man!"

"But I was found too soon. . . ."

Here he is! That thief is wearing clothing that he stole from this store!

Darn it! I'll be chased like a hunted rabbit again.

"I fought my way through different departments. . . ."

". . . .and finally had time to rest."

I should have done this in the first place. . .take off my clothes and become invisible!

The hunting party is here, but too late to stop me.

Look! Something flying through the air! The thief must have run behind something. Find him!

"They looked everywhere but where I was."

While they waste their time looking for me, I'll have breakfast. . .without paying.

"As the store became busier, I left it the same way I had entered . . .unclothed."

That plan failed. Anyway, the snow stopped and the sun is out, drying the sidewalks so I can walk around freely. But what shall I do next?

As Griffin continued his amazing tale to Dr. Kemp. . . .

At that moment, I sadly came to know that being invisible was not all good; it had many things against it! With bare skin I was freezing. . .yet wearing clothes made me ugly without a face. . .if I ate too much the undigested food would give me away. . .dogs could smell me with their noses. . .snow would show my footprints.

What was worse, I could see how rain would show my human form. . .fog would turn me into a visible ghost. . . even dust and soot falling on my skin would make me visible again.

"But finally, another answer to my problem came to me. . . ."

I can dress up if I cover my invisible head and face with a wig and false beard! I'll get them in this shop, and clothes too.

"The shopkeeper had heard the bell door tinkle, but when he came out...."

Some boys must have opened the door, I guess.

Now's my chance to slip upstairs where he lives.

"But I had to stay still when the shopkeeper returned to his lunch."

I've caught a cold but I mustn't sneeze...ah, stopped it just in time!

"The next time he left to serve a customer...."

I'll warm the place up so my cold won't get worse. Then I'll look around the house for clothes.

"But while I was looking through some old clothes...."

The shopkeeper ...with a gun!

I swear I heard a noise up here. But the room's empty.

But I need money too. I'll take the old man's collection of gold coins.

"But my new disguise led to another problem...."

I can't eat unless I remove my mask and that would show my invisible face! I'm starving... yet I can't touch that food!

"I went to another place and ordered a private room...."

At last I can feed myself!

"Later, I went to the Great Portland Street Post Office and claimed my package...." With my notes I'll experiment and find a way to become visible again. Being invisible all the time has too many problems. I'll rent a room in some small town and buy chemicals with the stolen money.

MAIL

As Griffin's strange story ended. . . .

So that was how I came to Iping and the Coach and Horses Inn. But it was a mistake to get that hobo, Thomas Marvel, to help me. He not only took money from me, but also hid my three notebooks. Now I need a new partner. . . .

. . . .you, Kemp! With your help I can take over town after town! To begin with, I'll kill anybody who gets in my way until I run this town. Are you with me?

He'll want to kill to get power! What shall I say?

But Dr. Kemp was saved from answering when. . . .

Wait! I hear footsteps coming upstairs!

Nonsense! it's your imagination.

But I hope it's Colonel Adye!

You tricked me! It's the police, isn't it? I'll toss off my robe and slip away as the Invisible Man.

No, you won't! I'll lock you in here!

But as luck would have it. . . .

The key fell on the floor! I can't reach it. I'll hold the door shut myself.

Let me out, Kemp!

As the two men fought, the door opened six inches. . . .

Ah, got you by the throat, Kemp! Now I'll make you let go of the door.

Ukk!

Kemp was flung back. . . .

Here's your robe. Now I'm invisible and can escape whoever you called to capture me.

Climbing the stairs, Colonel Adye was pushed out of the way. . . .

Out of my way, officer!

When Dr. Kemp had recovered. . . .

My God! The Invisible Man got away!

Tell me the whole story, Kemp.

After the doctor explained it all. . . .

. . . .and so, the Invisible Man plans to kill and injure people to get power! Colonel, you must stop him from leaving this town.

I'll have men guard the railroad stations and all roads. We'll get him.

The whole countryside joined the police in guarding every way of escape. . . .

That Invisible Man won't get past us!

Even if we don't see him, our dogs will pick up his smell!

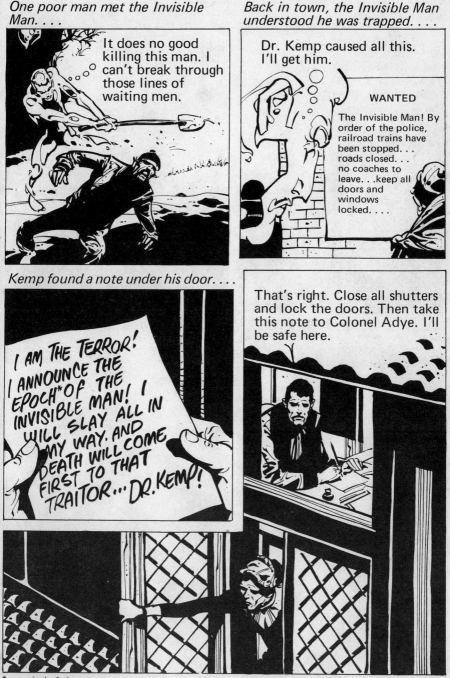

One poor man met the Invisible Man. . . .

It does no good killing this man. I can't break through those lines of waiting men.

Back in town, the Invisible Man understood he was trapped. . . .

Dr. Kemp caused all this. I'll get him.

WANTED

The Invisible Man! By order of the police, railroad trains have been stopped. . . roads closed. . . no coaches to leave. . .keep all doors and windows locked. . . .

Kemp found a note under his door. . . .

I AM THE TERROR! I ANNOUNCE THE EPOCH* OF THE INVISIBLE MAN! I WILL SLAY ALL IN MY WAY. AND DEATH WILL COME FIRST TO THAT TRAITOR... DR. KEMP!

That's right. Close all shutters and lock the doors. Then take this note to Colonel Adye. I'll be safe here.

* period of time

Some time later. . . .

And it came with a loud noise. . . .

Colonel Adye decided to go to the police station for help, but. . . .

Shortly after, Kemp let in his maid and two policemen she brought back. . . .

But that door was chopped down too, and then. . . .

Look! The Invisible Man is chopping down the kitchen door!

Quick! Into the dining room. I'll lock this door behind us.

Ah! I hit his invisible arm and made him drop the gun.

As the brave policeman swung again at his invisible enemy. . . .

I'll strike you sooner or later!

Oops! He's getting close.

My axe will finish you!

But the other policeman grabbed up the poker. . . .

That made you drop the axe!

I'm unarmed now. I've got to slip out of the house and get Kemp later.

When the policeman looked for Dr. Kemp. . . .

Our enemy must have left, Dr. Kemp. . .huh?

He's not here. He left with the maid in fear that the Invisible Man would finish us off and get him.

When Dr. Kemp ran to a neighbor's house for help. . . .

Help!

I won't let you in! I don't want the Invisible Man inside my house. Go away!

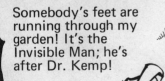

Somebody's feet are running through my garden! It's the Invisible Man; he's after Dr. Kemp!

The doctor tried any trick to slow down the killer.

But one of the workmen threw his shovel through the air. . . .

Ah, I struck that Invisible Man! Come on, men, let's all jump him now.

We got him! Hold him down!

But the Invisible Man's fighting suddenly stopped and a strange sight met their wondering eyes.

He's wounded and dying! And his body is becoming visible!

WORDS TO KNOW

digested	insane	puzzled
disguise	invisible	transparent
hobo		

QUESTIONS

1. Why did the Invisible Man move into the Coach and Horses Inn?

2. List some things done by the Invisible Man that tell you he was insane.

3. What is a hobo?

4. What two things did Griffin use to become invisible?

5. What were some disadvantages to being invisible?

6. How were dogs able to follow the Invisible Man?

7. Why did the Invisible Man need the help of the hobo?

8. What made the Invisible Man visible again?

9. How did the Invisible Man pay his rent in the Coach and Horses Inn?

10. Why did the Invisible Man wrap his pipe in a scarf when he smoked?